GRADE

# 04

# SINGING

12 songs for Trinity College London exams
from 2023

Published by
Trinity College London Press Ltd
trinitycollege.com
Registered in England
Company no. 09726123

First impression, March 2023



Cover design: Rod Steele
Printed in England by Caligraving Ltd

**Parental and Teacher Guidance:**
We recommend that parents and teachers exercise their own judgement to satisfy themselves that the lyrics of selected songs are appropriate for the students concerned. As you will be aware, there is no requirement that all songs in this syllabus must be learned. Trinity does not associate itself with, adopt or endorse any of the opinions or views expressed in the selected songs.

# Performance notes

## The Sound of Music from *The Sound of Music* / Rodgers & Hammerstein — Page 7

- Classic music theatre
- Lyrical
- Balanced register control

'The Sound of Music' is by Richard Rodgers and Oscar Hammerstein and is from the stage musical of the same name. The show is based on the 1946 memoirs of Maria von Trapp, a novice nun who became governess to Captain Georg von Trapp's children.

Maria Rainer (her real name was Kutchera) is a novice nun, and although she does want to take holy orders, she cannot escape the freedom that wandering in the hills around the convent gives her. Maria is regretful as she is reminded of the beautiful hills where she grew up and sings 'The Sound of Music'.

The opening bars up to the refrain (bar 20) are very much in the style of recitative (a style of writing a narrative or dialogue in the natural patterns of speech). Even though there is a rhythmic accompaniment from bar 10 you could still keep a feeling of internalising the thoughts, as if hoping for a sign, as the lyrics would suggest, that could keep her out in the open.

With the phrases being on repeated pitches (from bar 10) it helps to say the words as a monologue beforehand to find out which words are most important, so that singing in the same (spoken) rhythm and energy will give the lyrics more interest and will not sound like a boring monotone.

When the refrain starts the dynamic swells and it would be good to think of the opening bars (20–23) as one phrase. To help this effect, maintain the breath support through the rest in bar 21. It is also good practice to think of phrases as running from punctuation to punctuation, rather than from rest to rest, so maintaining breath support through the rests in the following two phrases will help the sense of flow. This is achieved by keeping the core muscles engaged through and beyond the first section of the phrase.

In bar 26 you could add a *crescendo* to help to get into the joy of 'the hills fill my heart'. This could be achieved by increasing the flow of air through extra support in the lower abdominal and control in the upper abdominal to prevent the pitch going sharp. This will also give a 'whoosh' for the phrase in bar 27.

In bar 34 it would help to maintain the flow of the mood with a gentle rise and fall in dynamic on that long note, with support right the way through to the end of the note.

The ***mp*** section (from bar 35) could indicate through the lyrics a feeling of wishing to make the same sounds as the landscape around, eg, getting louder from bar 50 'lark learning to pray'. It is most important when singing *forte* that you do not try to sing too loudly, but have a balanced control with the air supported. Singing 'too loud' can create an ugly sound; the great operatic soprano Dame Isobel Baillie once said: 'I never sing louder than lovely.'

Bar 51 starts ***mp*** with *crescendos* later, maintain a well-rounded sound (think of it as a lifting of emotion, therefore coming from deep within), then the *dim.* at bar 64 could imply a realisation that she must go back to the convent.

This song is about excitement at being out in the open and the work on breath support from the lower abdomen and getting the upper notes easily into *passaggio*, which is where the voice transitions through the middle section of the voice to reach the higher range. *(SMS)*

## Colors of the Wind from *Pocahontas* / Schwartz & Menken — Page 12

- Animated film
- Dramatic text
- Dynamic contrasts

'Colors of the Wind' is from *Pocahontas* which is a Disney story of the Powhatan princess, Pocahontas, and her meeting with John Smith. He was an English explorer, who in 1607 set out to create an English settlement in Jamestown, Virginia. Pocahontas is a native of this area and doesn't seem to take kindly to John Smith.

In this song Pocahontas is telling John that she is not the ignorant savage that he thinks she is, but that everybody belongs to the land, not the other way round.

The beginning has a feeling of disdain for John Smith's attitude of 'sovereignty' over the land, and that he considers himself above the 'natives' whom he calls savages. The beginning sections, bars 9–17, could be performed almost like a teacher talking to a child who hasn't understood the last lesson, so you might like to add some emphasis to certain words. In bars 10 to 12, both times, the words could be sung quite angrily but the second phrases (13–16) could be a bit calmer. There are no changes of dynamic markings written, but by concentrating on the meaning of the lyrics you will be able to decide how loudly or softly you would like to sing.

With the refrain (bar 18) you could lift the dynamic to ask the questions about nature of the self-styled 'civilised' man, and the repeat of the last phrase 'paint with all the colors of the wind' could be slightly held back and brought back to ***mp*** or even softer.

From bar 30 onwards a lesson is being taught with passion for the subject. You might like to add some excitement to the delivery and use the lower abdominal to engage that feeling of 'I love where I live!'

In bar 50 the question is more of a statemnet, since there is no answer, but you could raise the dynamic to the repeat of the 'wolf cry' section in bars 54 and 55, coming down on bar 62 to ***mp***. The last phrase finishes off the 'lesson' quite firmly but not loudly, but with the energy of a passionate teacher.

It is worth listening to the first section of the song which is not printed here to give you a context of the opening phrases. *(SMS)*

### Electricity from *Billy Elliot: The Musical* / Hall & John **Page 19**

- Contemporary musical theatre
- Conversational singing
- Characterisation

'Electricity' is from *Billy Elliot the Musical* (2005) written by Elton John with words by Lee Hall, based on the 2000 film which is about a boy from a mining town during the miners' strikes of the 1980s who wants to dance.

Billy takes a trip to audition for the Royal Ballet School. After the audition, and as he is about to leave, he is thinking that he has completely failed to impress the panel, but is asked 'Billy, how do you feel when you are dancing?' This song is his answer.

The song starts hesitantly, as though Billy is getting his thoughts together. You could try speaking the words before singing to get a measure of how unsure you are of the reason for feeling as you do. It is like a recitative, where the singer has more freedom of expression and is slightly more in control of the tempo because of the pauses.

In bar 10, when the tempo becomes more strict, there is still a feeling of trying to find the right words. The *crescendo* from bar 13 is gradual and should be well controlled with lower abdominal support to avoid the temptation to explode at the top, but when it comes to the first 'electricity' (bar 19), Billy realises it is the word that he has been searching for and the song then becomes more alive and driving. In bar 18 and 19, to support the Bs, use a bit of side muscle above the waist.

In the second verse, from bar 25, there is more emotion propelling the song. Words such as 'angry', 'scared', 'empty', 'full', should be emphasised to point up the contradictions in emotions – with great core support, so that you never feel that you have to shout, until the very last 'free', which is spoken.

*(SMS)*

### How Far I'll Go from *Moana* / Miranda **Page 26**

- Disney animation
- Vocal control
- Emotional contrasts

'How Far I'll Go' is from the film *Moana*, by Lin-Manuel Miranda. He also wrote *In the Heights* (2005), *Hamilton* (2015) and the soundtrack of Disney's *Encanto* (2021).

*Moana* is an animated film set in ancient Polynesia and based on Polynesian mythology. Moana is a sea-faring queen on a mission to save her island from a terrible curse.

This is a song about conflicting emotions and calling. Moana wants to be a good queen because that is her heritage but she keeps getting drawn to the sea without knowing why.

The start is quite hesitant, asking questions, up to bar 12 when you think that whatever you do, you still come back to the sea. Keep the *crescendo* in bar 15 controlled because there is a long way to go in the song.

Every time you get to the phrase 'it calls me' give it a feeling of wanting to follow the call but still not understanding why.

You could add a *diminuendo* in bar 23 to come back to a more spoken style of delivery in bar 24, talking about the island and the people.

In bar 32 be more confident about fulfilling the role of queen, but in bars 34 & 35 the doubt creeps back in, however the *forte* at bar 35 could demonstrate the call of the sea and what it is doing to the emotions. Make sure that the *crescendo* in bar 44 is gradual so that the last phrase is very controlled and not shouted. This requires good lower abdominal support.

*(SMS)*

### Where the Bee Sucks / Shakespeare & Arne **Page 32**

- Dotted rhythms
- Terraced dynamics
- Ornamentation

The text for 'Where the Bee Sucks' is by Shakespeare from *The Tempest* and, in this play, the words are delivered by the character Ariel, who is a lively spirit, full of magical powers.

There are a number of dotted rhythms in this song and often these rhythms are used to give a feeling of energy and propulsion to phrases. It can be tricky to get these absolutely precise so explore different rhythmic exercises with your teacher, speaking as well as singing, to achieve rhythmic security.

'Where the Bee Sucks' comes from the Baroque era of music and in songs of this period you often find terraced dynamics. This is where there is a sudden change between dynamics rather than the gradual shift you would get with a *crescendo* or *diminuendo*. You could think of it like taking a quick step up or down a staircase. Try playing with this effect on the words: 'where owls do cry'.

In Baroque singing it would also have been common practice for the performer to add some variations, or embellishments, to the melody when it repeats. Here there are opportunities to add your own additions in both the first and the second verses so you could think about passing notes, suspensions or mordents for example.

As you progress with your singing you might like to look at 'I attempt from Love's Sickness' by Purcell, which you will find in the Trinity Grade 5 book, as it has similar musical and technical characteristics. *(LH)*

### On the Banks of Allan Water / Lewis, *arr.* Moore **Page 36**

- Story telling
- *Tenuto* markings
- Flow

'On the Banks of Allan Water' is the sad tale of Miller's daughter who has been betrayed by a loved one and dies from a broken heart. Allan Water is a river in central Scotland and this song suggests the ebb and flow of the water, particularly in the movement of the quavers, which appear so frequently in the piano accompaniment.

There are three verses to this song and all are virtually the same in notes and rhythms. But, as the story unfolds the mood changes quite dramatically and you can explore different ways to use your voice to communicate the emotions. Try perhaps keeping the tonal colour bright and resonant for first verse then notice the change of dynamic for verse 2 and then the change of tempo. Imagine the cold of a harsh winter as you sing verse 3 and plan how quietly and how slowly you will sing the very last phrase of the piece where the repeated notes might suggest the tolling of a funeral bell.

Another expressive tool you can use are the many *tenuto* marks in the music. For instrumentalists these signs are directions to sustain a note for its full length but for singers, *tenuto* marks are often indications that words should receive some degree of emphasis. So you can experiment with different ways of conveying the important words in the text.

Overall, this song needs a good sense of flow as suggested by the *fluente* direction. Think of how each phrase unfolds and the direction the music takes to help you feel the forward movement of the music. *(LH)*

## The Gentle Dove / Williams — Page 42

- Breath management
- Rhythmic variety
- Changing tempi

The words of 'The Gentle Dove' suggest a person who is unrequited in love but the lively, upbeat feel to the music carries a sense of hope that all may be resolved in the end.

There are some long phrases in this song and you will need to plan when you are going to breathe. Sometimes you might find that you need to take an extra breath, so think about the meaning of the words and try to ensure that the sense of a line is not interrupted. You will also want to make sure that your intake is quick and unobtrusive so, technically, you could practise breathing in quickly without any constriction in the throat. Loosening the abdominal muscles as you breathe in can also help to avoid any unwanted tightening.

Within the phrases there is much rhythmic variety with some crochet / quaver patterns, semiquavers and dotted motifs all adding 'bounce' to the music. You could try listening to the recording and clapping the rhythms as you listen before then singing along to the recording to check if you are in time.

Experiment with the different tempi markings too, to see how you feel the *poco ralls*, *ralls* and *a tempo* directions help to add expression to the emotion of the song.

Doves are often seen as symbols of peace and love, or new beginnings, across different cultures and religions. You could see how these themes are explored in other songs about doves that you can find. *(LH)*

## Go 'Way from my Window / Trad. *arr.* Schram — Page 46

- Rhythmic freedom
- Held notes
- Pitching

'Go 'Way from my Window' is an American song from the early twentieth century, originally ascribed to John Jacob Niles. Ruth Elaine Schram's arrangement was made much later but still retains the wonderful folk-like simplicity of the vocal line.

The marking at the opening of *ad lib*, suggest that the singer can have some flexibility in approaching the pulse and the rhythms. There is a fine line here between being too free so that the music loses cohesion or too rigid so that the music loses expression. The other direction at the beginning: *with feeling* may help you to decide how to manage your performance. Think of the emotion behind the words and the way the melody line naturally rises and falls and you will start to find your own artistic expression.

Avoid cutting the long, held notes too short otherwise there will be gaps in the music. This is especially true at the end of the song. Building up your breath stamina can help, so try releasing the air evenly and without pushing, practising with some different sounds such as 'ss' (/s/) or 'zz' (/z/).

There are some semitones to negotiate in the vocal line too and, while the piano accompaniment is supportive, some preparatory exercises incorporating parts of a chromatic scale will help you to get used to pitching these small intervals.

'Go 'Way from my Window' has been recorded by many different artists, including John Jacob Niles himself, and it might be interesting to listen to them and see how he and others have interpreted this song. *(LH)*

## Clouds / Mandel — Page 50

- Jazz rhythms
- Clear text
- Phrasing

Ellen Mandel is a composer and pianist based in New York, specialising in art song, and heavily influenced by jazz. This melancholy and nostalgic song needs an improvisatory feel, with relaxed rhythms and very clear text.

The short phrases need to be *legato* throughout, with arch shaped phrasing – growing towards the middle of each phrase and then dying away. Try to find a different dynamic and tone colour for each iteration of the word 'remember'.

It would be useful to listen to (and perform) some jazz standards while learning this song, to help with the sense of style. Songs such as 'Autumn Leaves' and 'Summertime' would be good songs to help work on the rhythms and flexibility that is crucial in this song.

Breaths should only be taken when you have rests, except for bar 54. A breath before the final 'remember' will help create a strong and confident ending. *(H/KA)*

### **Dihumbwa** / Unaeb — Page 54

- Echo dynamics
- Octave leaps
- Melismatic quaver runs

Engelhardt Unaeb is a composer from Namibia in West Africa, specialising in choral music. This song sets a short proverb in Mbukushu, a Bantu language, about the cheetah.

This is a fun, lively song with a very fast tempo. Learn the song at a slower speed, working carefully on the pronunciation before you gradually speed it up to the intended tempo. The repeated phrases act as echoes, so, once you are secure with the notes and lyrics, work on making a clear difference between the *forte* and *mezzo piano* phrases. Take care that pitches don't sink flat at the softer dynamic.

The octave leaps are particularly tricky; make sure you have the high note in mind as you start each phrase. The quaver runs in bars 60–61 and 69–70 will need slow practice. Try practicing them using dotted quavers and semiquavers to make sure you are in the middle of every note, with an even tone. When it is secure with dotted rhythms, revert to the printed quavers. Most importantly, enjoy yourself – this is a virtuosic showstopper and great fun to sing! *(H/KA)*

### **Caro mio ben** / Giordani — Page 58

- Italianate vowels
- *Legato* line
- Baroque phrasing

This is one of the most well-known Italian Baroque arias, having been recorded many times. It was composed in London in the 1780s by the Italian composer Giuseppe Giordani, who later moved to Dublin where he spent the rest of his life. Although it has the feel of an opera aria, it is in fact a stand-alone love song.

This is an excellent song for practising your *legato* line and ensuring that you are always producing an even and consistent tone. Try practising the whole song to 'zzzz' or a rolled 'r' if you can. Make sure the sound doesn't have any lumps and bumps and that the air flow is smooth. This is especially important in the phrases which include larger intervals.

There are a lot of descending phrases in this piece, so care is needed to ensure that flatness doesn't creep in. The Italian vowels need to be very bright, particularly the 'a' vowels, which require a higher tongue position than you would normally have when speaking English. When the main tune returns towards the end you can explore the idea of adding some light ornamentation to add interest. *(H/KA)*

### **Gia la notte s'avvicina** / Colbran — Page 62

- Italianate vowels
- *Legato* line
- Semitone intonation

Isabella Colbran was one of the most celebrated opera singers of her day and she worked with her husband, the composer Gioachino Rossini, to create some of his most famous roles. She published four volumes of songs, one of which is this delightful barcarolle. Barcarolles are songs composed in the style of folk tunes sung by the Venetian gondoliers, always in a lilting $\frac{6}{8}$ time signature. This particular text has been set many other times, including by Ludwig van Beethoven.

Like 'Caro mio ben', this song needs the bright, Italianate vowels with a high position of the back of your tongue, particularly in the 'a' vowels on 'respirar' and 'mar'. Practise the whole song to a rolled 'r' or 'zzz' to check the consistency of the air flow and to feel the support in your lower abdominal muscles.

When you have notes above a D on an 'e' or 'i' vowel (for example 'marina') you will need to drop your tongue a tiny bit to avoid those vowels sounding squeaky. The paired quavers need elegant phrasing and lightening off. Feel free to take your time over the second half of bar 24 to help add to the inviting nature of this song! *(H/KA)*

authors: *(SMS)* Simon Masterton-Smith, *(LH)* Luise Horrocks, *(H/KA) Helen and Kate Ashby*

[Blank page to facilitate page turns]

# The Sound of Music

from *The Sound of Music*

Oscar Hammerstein II
1895–1960

Richard Rodgers
1902–1979

**Molto moderato (tenderly)** ♩ = *c.*108

*mp*

My day in the hills has come to an end, I

**Molto moderato (tenderly)** ♩ = *c.*108

*p* *legato*

5

know. A star has come out to tell me it's time to go. But

10

deep in the dark green shad - ows are voic - es that urge me to

*sempre legato*

13

stay. So I pause and I wait and I lis - ten for one more sound, For



In the exam omit the repeat

17
cresc.
rit.
più rit.
one more love - ly thing that the hills might say.
rit.
più rit.
cresc.
Refrain
Moderately ♩ = c.132
mf
20
with warm expression
The hills are a - live with the sound of mu - sic,
Moderately ♩ = c.132
p
23
With songs they have sung for a thou - sand
26
years. The hills fill my heart with the sound of

30
mu - sic.
My heart wants to sing ev - 'ry song it
34
mp
hears.
My heart wants to beat like the wings of the
mp
37
birds that rise from the lake to the trees.
My
40
cresc.
heart wants to sigh like a chime that flies from a church on a
cresc.

43
mf
breeze, To laugh like a brook when it trips and falls o - ver
mf
46
stones on its way, to sing through the night like a
50
cresc.
mp
lark who is learn - ing to pray. I go to the hills
cresc.
mp
53
when my heart is lone - ly. I

56
cresc.
know I will hear what I've heard be - fore.
59
cresc.
My heart will be blessed with the sound of
mf più espressivo
62
dim.
mu - sic and I'll sing once
dim.
66
1.
2.
more. The more.
p
mp

Group A

# Colors of the Wind

from *Pocahontas*

Stephen Schwartz
b. 1948

Alan Menken
b. 1949

 In the exam do observe the repeats

13
1.
I know ev - 'ry rock and tree and crea-ture has a life, has a spir - it, has a
if you walk the foot-steps of a strang-er you'll learn
16
2.
mp
cresc.
name. You things_ you nev-er knew_ you nev-er knew. Have you
19
ev - er heard the wolf cry to the blue corn moon or asked the grin-ning bob-cat why he

22
f
mf
grinned? Can you sing with all__ the voic-es of the moun-tain? Can you
f
mf

25
mp
paint with all__ the col-ors of the wind? Can you paint with all__ the col-ors of the
mp

28
mf (verse 1)
f (verse 2)
wind? Come run the hid-den pine__ trails of the
rain-storm and the riv - er are my
mf-f

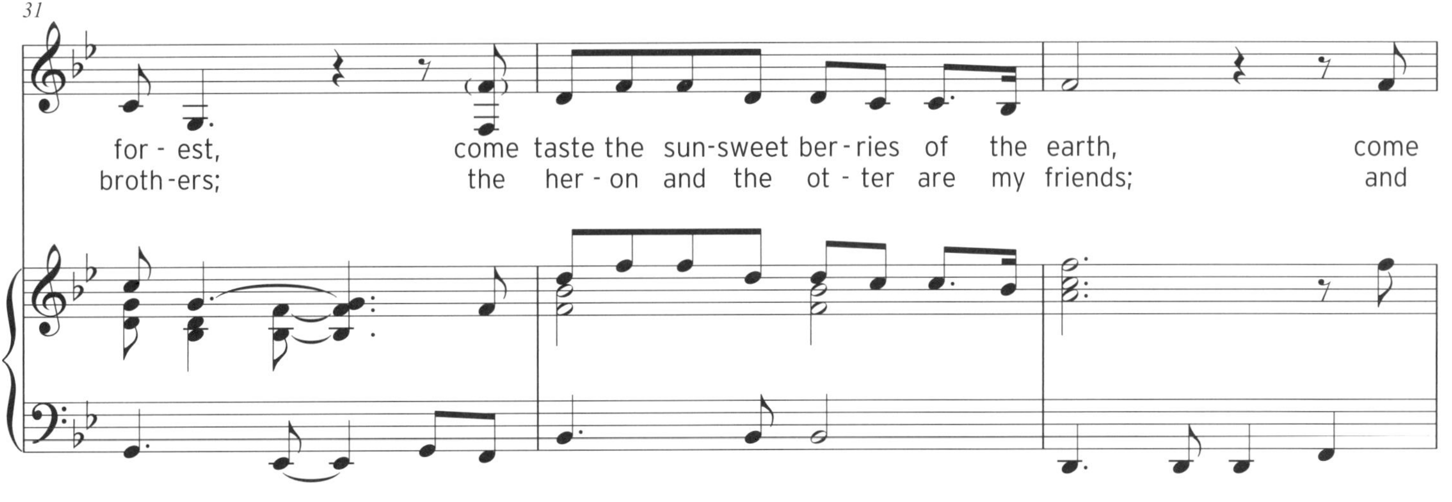
31
for - est,
broth-ers;
come taste the sun-sweet ber-ries of the earth,
the her - on and the ot - ter are my friends;
come
and

34
1.
roll in all__ the rich-es all a-round you,
we are all__ con-nect-ed to each oth - er
and for once nev-er won-der what they're
in a

37
2.
worth.
The cir - cle in a hoop that nev - er__ ends.
Have you

40
ev - er heard the wolf cry to the blue corn moon or let the ea - gle tell you where he's

43
mf
been? Can you sing with all__ the voic - es of the moun - tain? Can you
mf

46
mp
paint with all__ the col-ors of the wind? Can you paint with all__ the col-ors of the
mp

49
mf
wind? How high does the syc - a-more grow? If you
mf

52
3
rall.
cut it down then you'll nev - er know. And you'll
3
rall.

55
a tempo
nev - er hear the wolf cry to the blue corn moon, for wheth-er we are white or cop-per -
a tempo

58
dim.
-skinned, we need to sing with all__ the voic-es__ of the moun-tain, we need to
dim.
61
mp
paint with all__ the col-ors of the wind. You can own the earth and still all you'll
mp
64
p
Freely
a tempo
own is earth un-til you can paint with all the col-ors of the wind.
Freely
a tempo
p
67
rit.

# Electricity

from *Billy Elliot: The Musical*

Lee Hall
b. 1966

Elton John
b. 1947

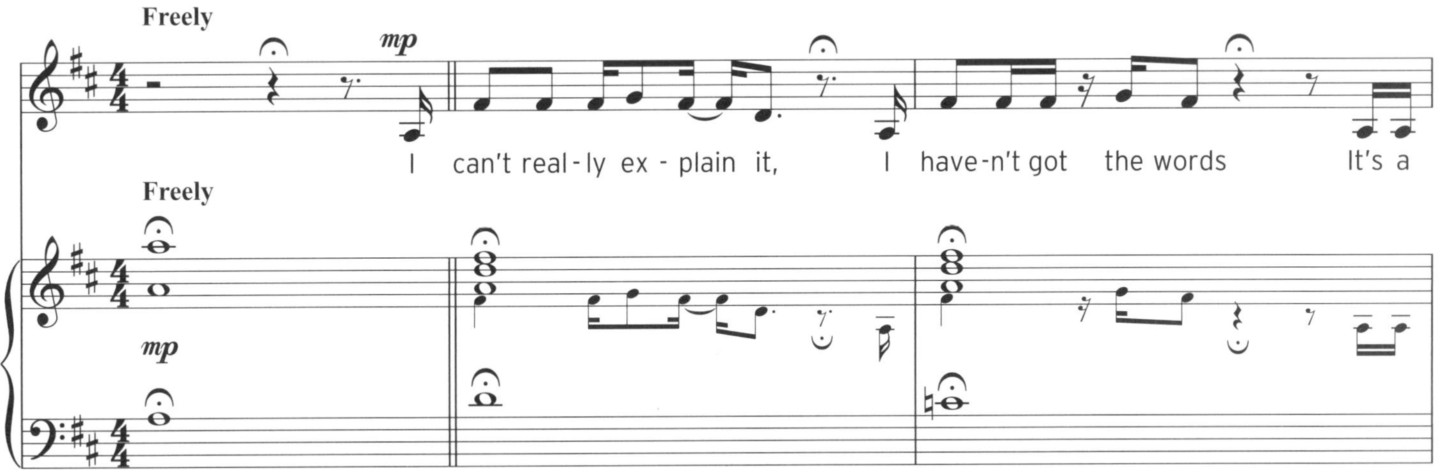


(Small notes in the piano part may be included for the exam if desired)

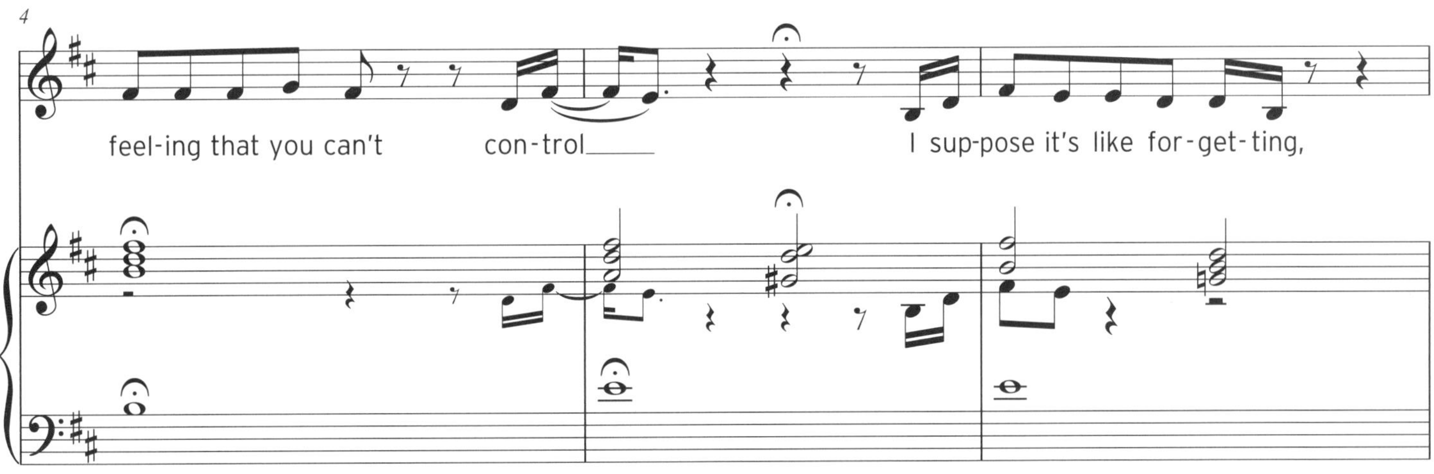


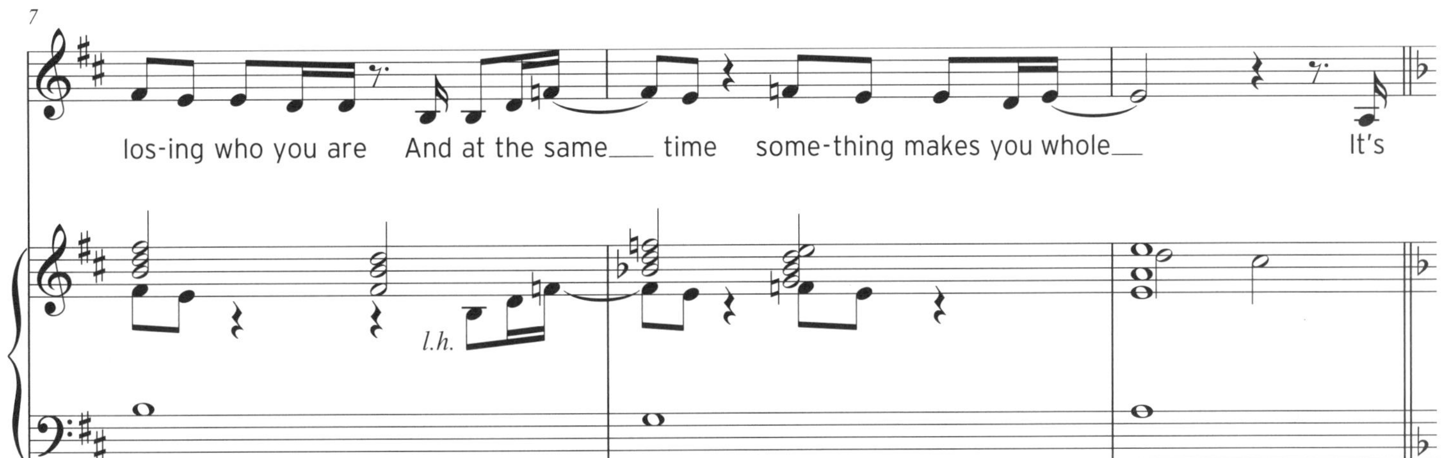

10
♩ = c.80
like that there's a mu - sic, play - ing in___ your ear And I'm
♩ = c.80
12
lis-tening, and I'm lis-tening and then I dis - ap-pear And then I
14
mf
feel a change Like a fire___ deep in - side__
mf
16
Some-thing burst - ing me wide o - pen Im - pos - si - ble__ to hide__ And

18
sud - den - ly___ I'm fly - ing
Fly - ing like a bird Like e - lec -
20
dim.
-tric - i - ty E - lec - tric - i - ty
Sparks in - side of me_ And I'm
23
mp
f
free I'm free
It's a
mf
26
bit like be - ing an - gry, it's a bit like be - ing scared Con -

28
mp
-fused and all mixed up and mad as hell__ It's
30
mp
like when you've been cry-ing And you're emp - ty and you're full I
32
don't know what it is, it's hard to tell It's
34
like that there's some mu - sic, play - ing in__ your ear But the

36
mu-sic is im - pos-si-ble, im-pos - si-ble__ to hear_ But then I
38
cresc.
feel it move me Like a burn-ing deep in - side__
f
40
Some-thing burst - ing me wide o-pen Im - pos - si - ble__ to hide_ And
f
42
sud-den - ly___ I'm fly - ing Fly - ing like a bird Like e - lec -

44
dim.
-tric - i - ty
E - lec - tric - i - ty
Sparks in -
ff
dim.
46
-side of me
And I'm free
I'm
free
49
f
molto rall.
Faster ♩ = 94
free
I'm
free!
molto rall.
Faster ♩ = 94
f
53
rall.
rall.

[Blank page to facilitate page turns]

Group A

# How Far I'll Go

from *Moana*

Words & music:
Lin-Manuel Miranda
b. 1980

**Moderately** ♩ = 84

*mp*

4 *mp*

I've been star - ing at the edge of the wa - ter__ long__ as I can re-

*p*

6

-mem-ber,__ nev-er real-ly know-ing why. I wish I could be the per-fect

9 *mf*

daugh-ter,__ but I come back to the wa - ter no mat-ter how hard I try. Ev-'ry

12
turn I take, ev-'ry trail I track, ev-'ry path I make, ev-'ry road leads back to the
14
cresc.
place I know where I can-not go, where I long ___ to be. See the
16
f
line where the sky meets the sea, it calls ___ me, and no one knows ___ how far it
f
19
goes. ___ If the wind in my sail on the sea stays be-hind ___ me, one day I'll

22
know.
If I go, there's just no tell-ing how far I'll
24
mp
go. I know ev-'ry-bod-y on this is-land seems so hap-py on this
mp
26
is-land. Ev-'ry-thing is by de-sign.
28
mf
I know ev-'ry-bod-y on this is-land has a role on this
mf

30
is - land, so may-be I can roll with mine. I can
32
cresc.
lead with pride, I can make us strong. I'll be sat - is - fied if I play a - long, but the
cresc.
34
f
voice in - side sings a dif - f'rent song. What is wrong with me?
f
36
mf
See the light as it shines on the sea: it's blind -
mf

38
- ing, but no one knows how deep it
40
goes. And it seems like it's call-ing out to me, so come find
42
me and let me know,
p
What's be -
44
f
-yond that line? Will I cross that line? The line where the sky meets the sea, it calls
p
f

46
— me, and no one knows how far it
48
goes. If the wind in my sail on the sea stays be - hind
50
— me, one day I'll know how far I'll
52
go!
sfz

# Where the Bee Sucks

William Shakespeare
1564–1616

Thomas Arne
1710–1778

 In the exam do observe the repeats

17
p
mf
couch when owls do cry, when owls do cry, when owls do cry. On a
p
mf
21
cresc.
bat's back do I fly, do I fly, Af - ter
25
1.
sun - set, mer-ri - ly, mer-ri - ly, Af - ter sun - set, mer - ri - ly.
1.
30
2.
- ly.
2.

34
f (1st time)
mp cresc. (2nd time)
Mer-ri - ly, mer-ri - ly shall I live now, Un - der the
f-mp cresc.
38
blos-som that hangs on the bough, Mer-ri - ly, mer-ri - ly shall I live now, Un - der the
42
rit. (2nd time)
(a tempo)
blos-som that hangs on the bough, Un - der the blos-som that hangs on the bough.
rit. (2nd time)
(a tempo)
46
rit.
rit.

[Blank page to facilitate page turns]

# On the Banks of Allan Water

Matthew Lewis
1775-1818

Trad.
*arr.* Philip Moore

13
bride a sol-dier sought her, and a win - ning tongue had_ he;___ On the
17
banks of Al - lan Wa - ter, none so fair as she.
21
p
2. On the
p
25
banks of Al - lan Wa - ter when brown Au - tumn spreads it's___

28
store, There I saw the mil - ler's daugh - ter, but she smiled no
32
more. For the Sum - mer grief had brought her, and her sol - dier false was
36
meno mosso
he; On the banks of Al - lan Wa - ter, none so sad as
meno mosso
40
a tempo
she.
a tempo
mf

44
mf
3. On the banks of Al - lan Wa - ter when the win - ter snow fell
48
fast, still was seen the mil - ler's daugh - ter, chil - ling blew the
52
blast. But the mil - ler's love - ly daugh - ter both from care and cold was
56
free, On the banks of Al - lan Wa - ter, there,

60
molto rall.
there a corpse lay she;
molto rall.
pp
63
pp
there a corpse lay she.

[Blank page to facilitate page turns]

Group B

# The Gentle Dove

Trad.
*arr.* Grace Williams
1906–1977

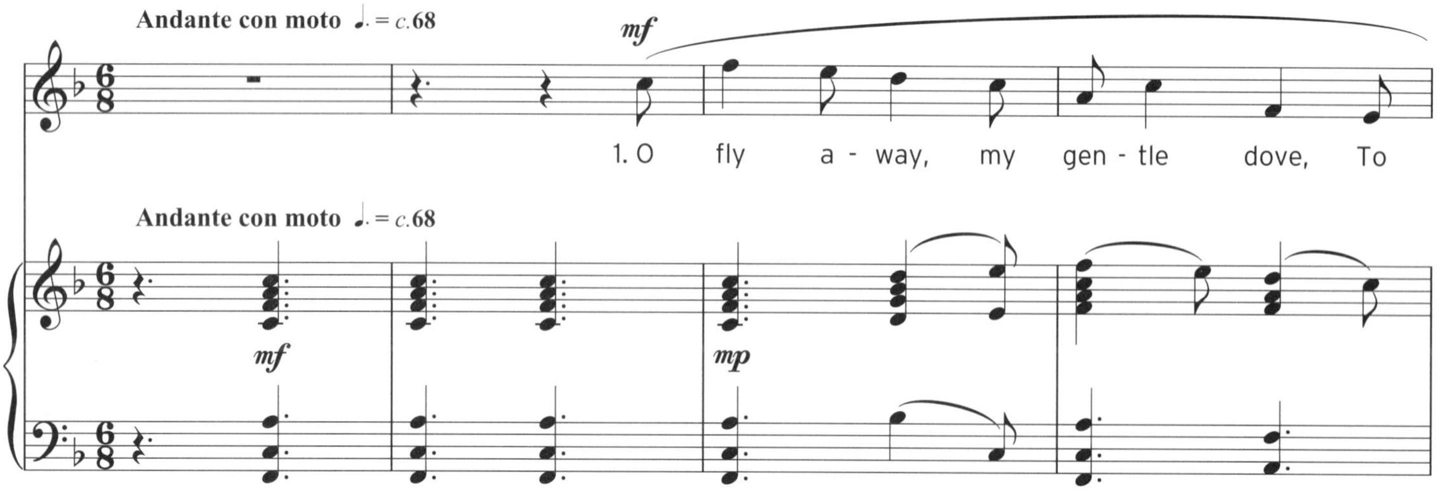

**Andante con moto** ♩. = *c.*68

*mf*

1. O fly a - way, my gen - tle dove, To

**Andante con moto** ♩. = *c.*68

*mf* *mp*

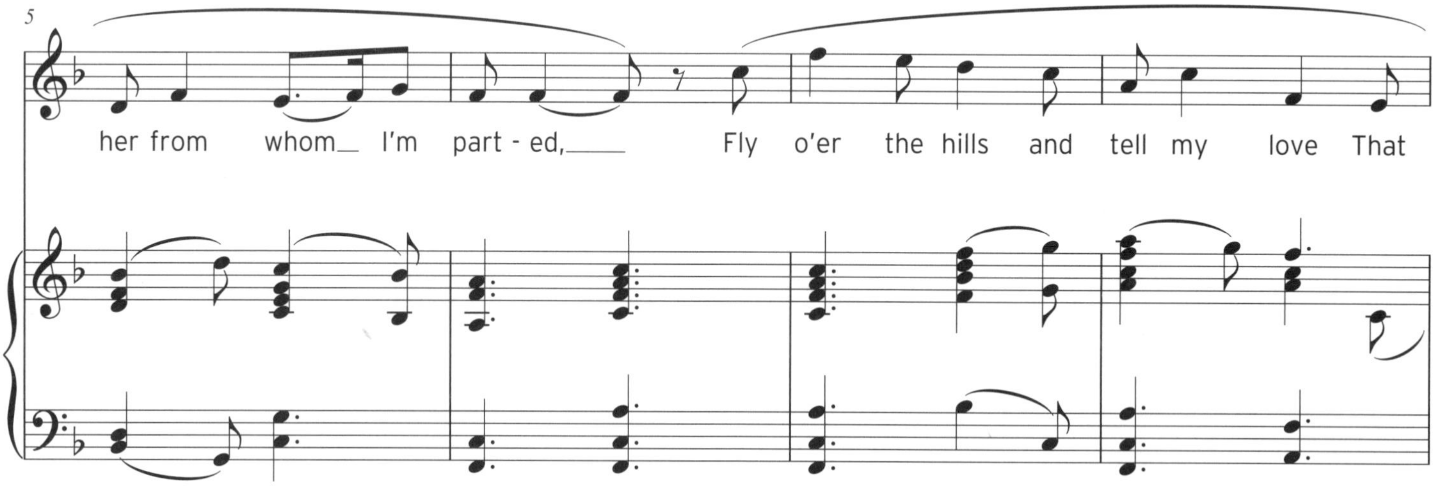

5

her from whom__ I'm part - ed,____ Fly o'er the hills and tell my love That

9

I am bro - ken - heart - ed.____ Tell her that I long to see her,

Ped. ✻ Ped.

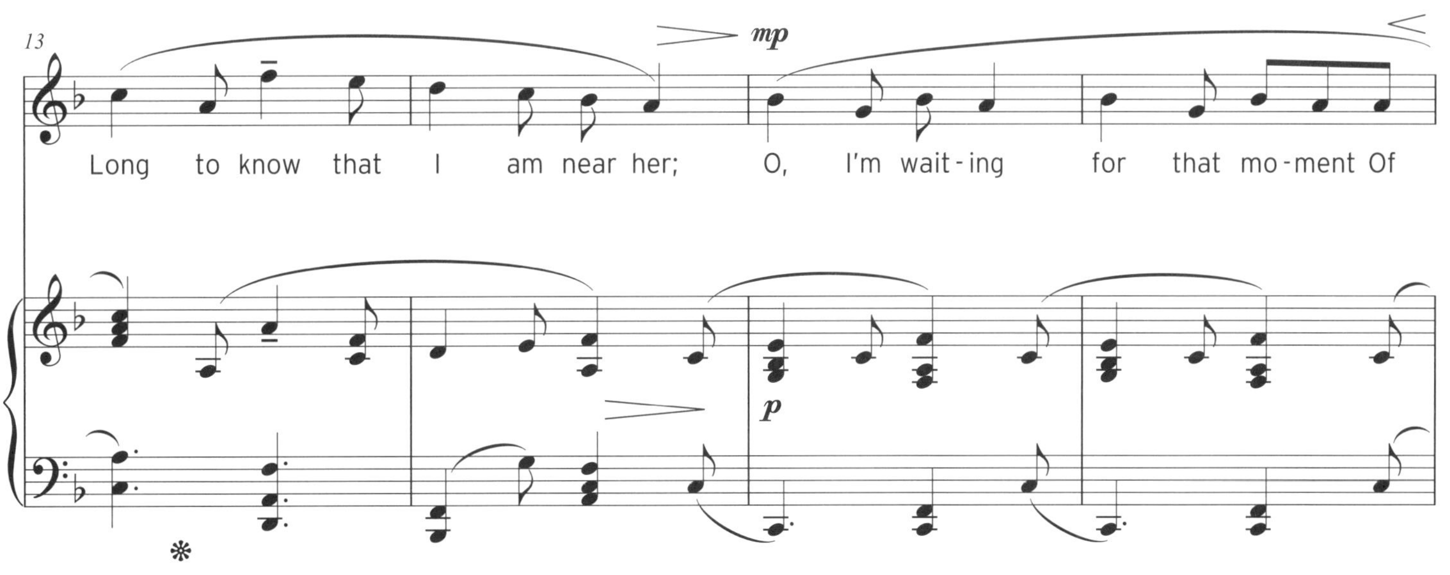
13
mp
Long to know that I am near her; O, I'm wait-ing for that mo-ment Of
p

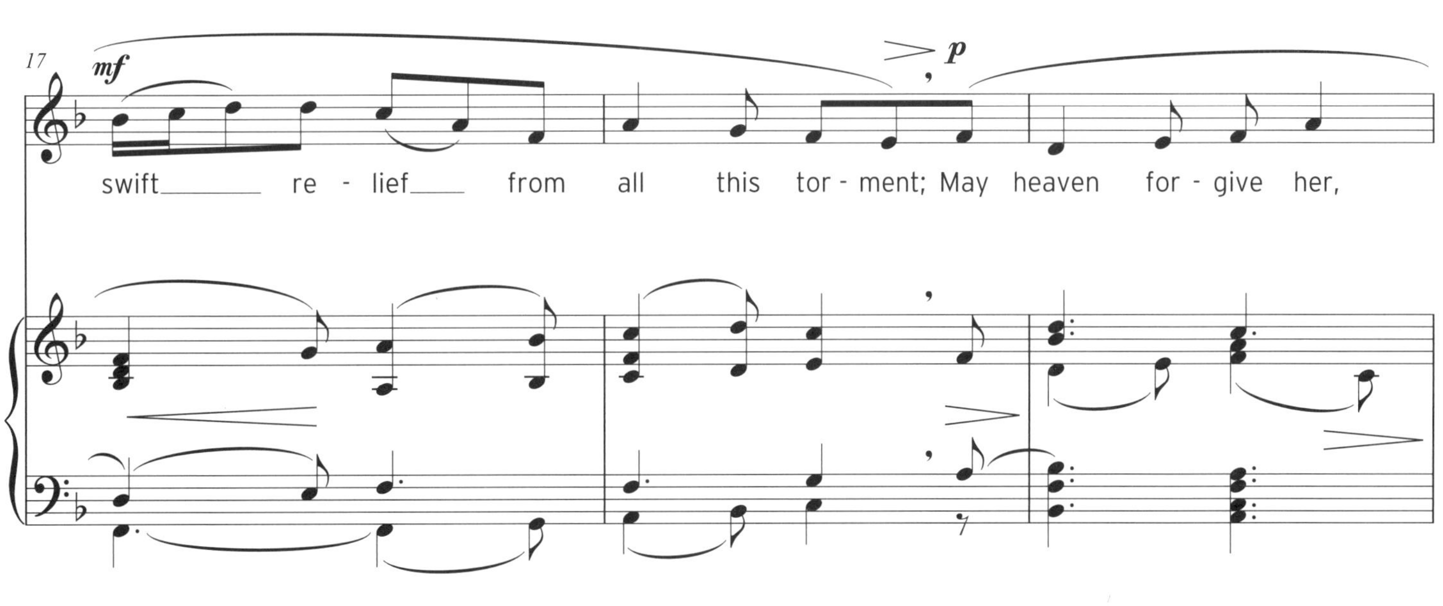
17
mf
p
swift re-lief from all this tor-ment; May heaven for-give her,

20
poco rall.
a tempo
mp
mf
for she knows My heart is ev - er fer-vent.
2. O,
poco rall.
a tempo
pp
p
mf

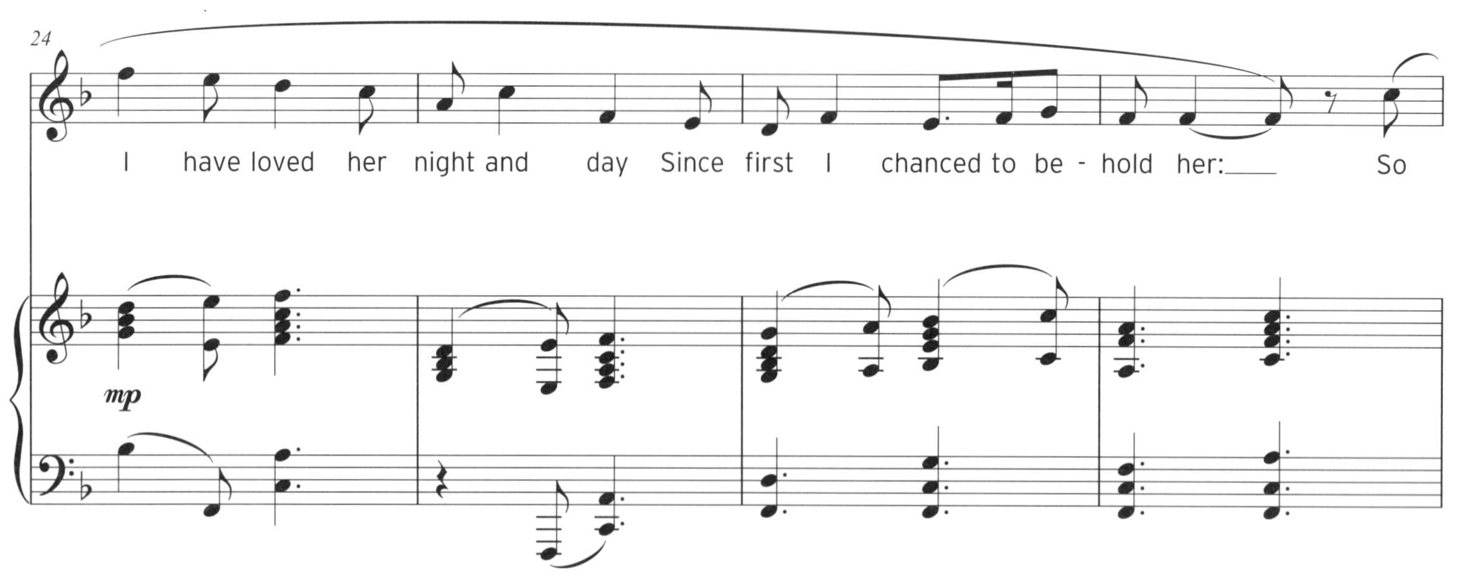
24
I have loved her night and day Since first I chanced to be - hold her: So
mp

28
light of foot she was, and gay, And beau - ty did en - fold her;
mf
mp
mf

32
O, she was so fair and slen - der And her smile so sweet and ten - der,
mp
mp
mf

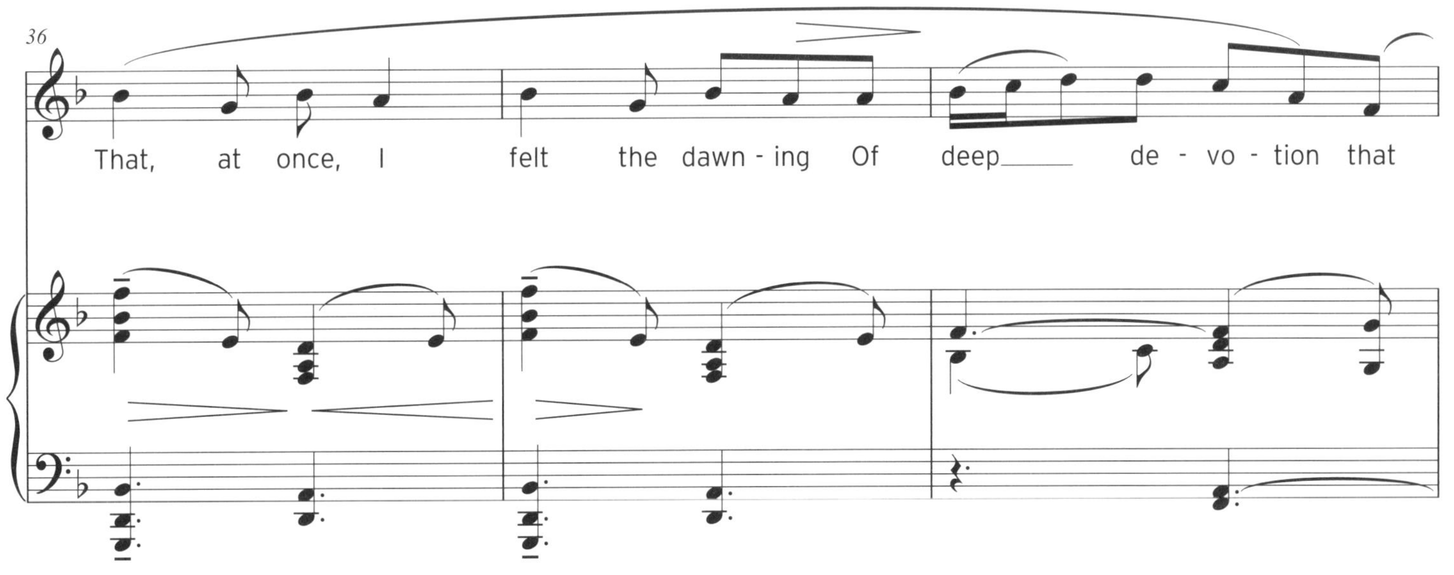
36
That, at once, I felt the dawn - ing Of deep de - vo - tion that

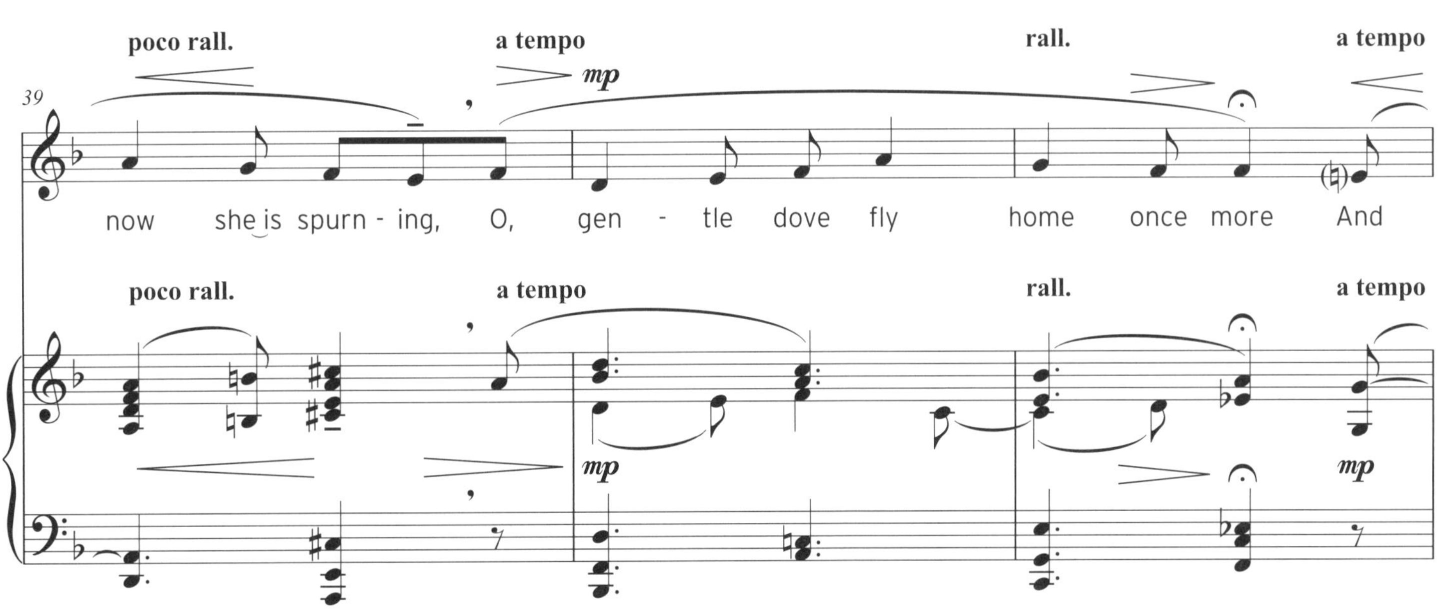
poco rall.
a tempo
mp
rall.
a tempo
39
now she is spurn - ing, O, gen - tle dove fly home once more And
poco rall.
a tempo
rall.
a tempo
mp
mp

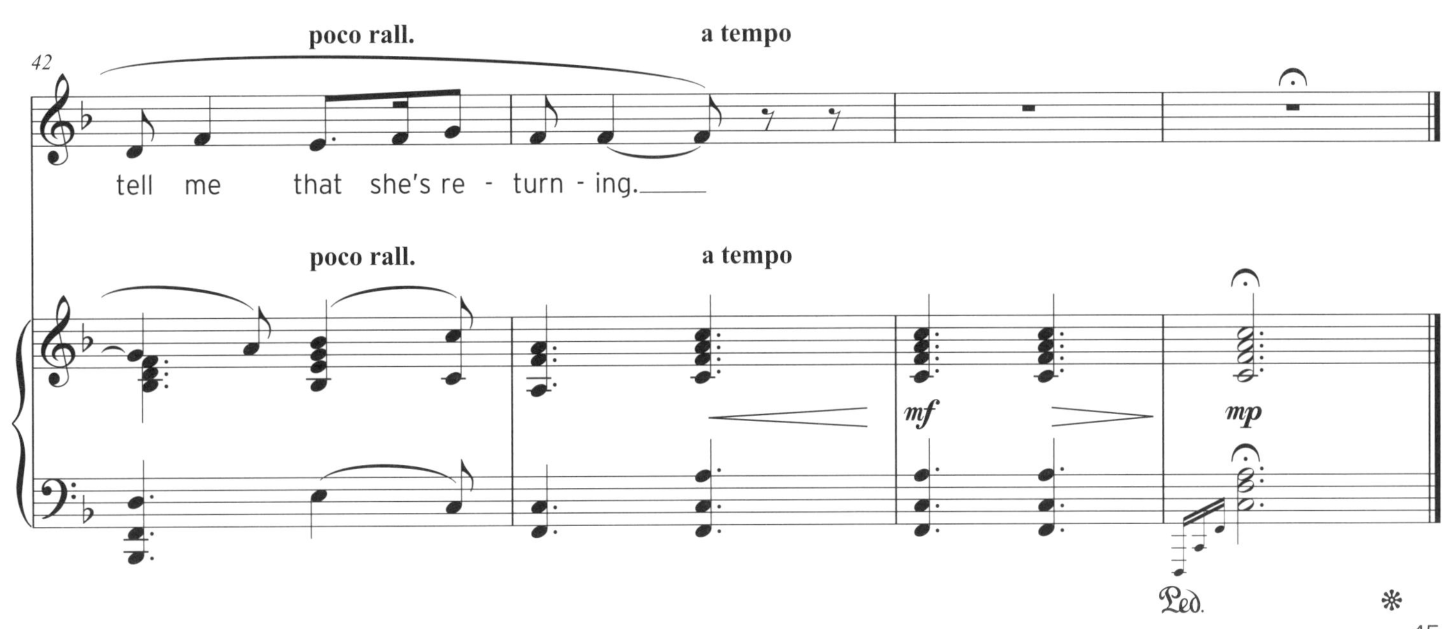
poco rall.
a tempo
42
tell me that she's re - turn - ing.
poco rall.
a tempo
mf
mp
Ped.

# Go 'Way from my Window

Group B

Trad.
*arr.* Ruth Elaine Schram

 In the exam do observe the repeat

a tempo
mp
both - er me no more. Go 'way from my win - dow.
now, my love, de - part. Go 'way from my win - dow.
a tempo
mp
mf
Go 'way from my win - dow.
Go 'way from my win - dow.
mf
1.
mp
2.
f
Go
Go
1.
2.
mp
cresc.
f
rall.
a tempo
'way from my win - dow, go a - way from my door, go
rall.
a tempo

rall.
'way, I wish you to leave me, and both - er me no
rall.
mf
Freely
more. Just both - - er me no
Freely
mf
(bring out melody)
Broadly
more. No more;
Broadly
mp
(opt.)
rit.
no more.
rit.
mp
r.h.
pp

[Blank page to facilitate page turns]

Group B

# Clouds

Words & music:
Ellen Mandel

17
mf
Clouds a - cross the sky
Tears fall from my eyes
3
mf
21
Ne - ver said good - bye
Re - mem - ber
mf
25
An - - gels,
so ma-ny an - - gels
29
f
Why can't we have them back a - gain?
f

33
An - - gels, so ma-ny an - - gels
37
Once they were here re-mem-ber them.
41
mf
mp
Clouds a-cross my mind
An-swers I can't find
45
You left me be-hind Re-mem - ber

49
mf
Clouds will drift_ a - way
Night will fol - low day
53
1 2
Love is here_ to stay
Re- mem - ber
57
mf
61

# Dihumbwa

HaMbukushu proverb translation:
*The cheetah catches the duiker (a small antelope) for pleasure or laughter, at first he follows it slowly, then he runs.*

Pronuciation:
*Dihumbwa = dee hoom bwah, dya = dee ah, kwatera = koo ah teh rah. mapi = mah pee, mumune = moo moo neh, mu mungwangu = moo moong goo ahng goo, mo mu kutjira = moh moo koo chi rah*

Trad.

Engelhardt Unaeb
b. 1984

 In the exam do observe the repeats

f (1st time)
mp (2nd time)
Di - hum - bwa dya kwa - te - ra
ma - pi mu-mu - ne,
f-mp
f
mo - mun - gwan - gu,
mo mu ka - tji - ra.
mp
Mo - mun - gwan - gu,
mo mu ka - tji - ra.

f (1st time)
mp (2nd time)
39
Di - hum-bwa dya kwa - te - ra ma - pi mu-mu - ne,
f-mp
45
f
Di - hum - bwa,
f
51
p
Di - hum - bwa,
p
f
Di - hum - bwa,
f
57
Di - hum - bwa.

63
p
Di - hum - bwa.
f
Di - hum - bwa.
69
75
81

Group C

# Caro mio ben

*My dearest love, believe me please, without you my heart languishes.*
*I, your faithful lover, yearn for you every hour.*
*Cease this cruel scorn.*

Words & music:
Giuseppe Giordani
1751-1798

**Larghetto**

**Larghetto**

**p** *dolce*

*largamente*

4

**p**

Ca - ro mio ben, cre - di - mi al - men, sen - za di te lan - gui - sce il

**p** *dolce*

8

cor, ca - ro mio ben, sen - za di te lan - gui - sce il

**f**

**p**

12
p
cor. Il tuo fe - del so - spi - ra o -
f
p

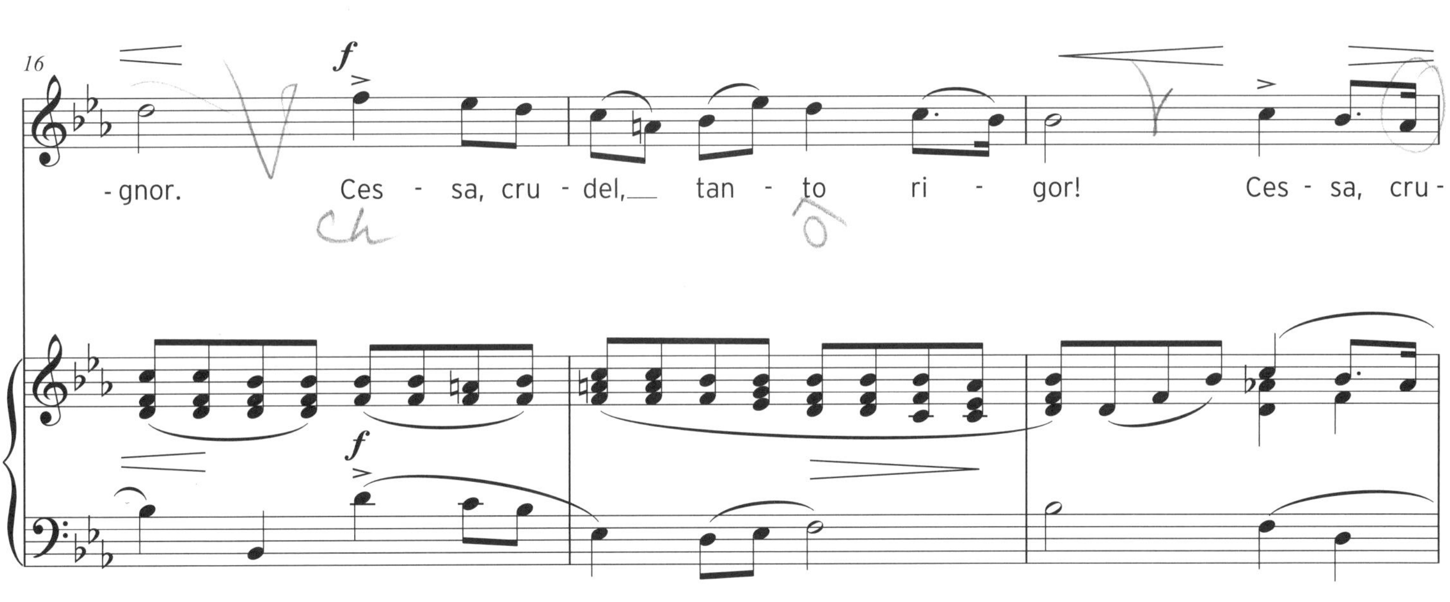
16
f
-gnor. Ces - sa, cru - del, tan - to ri - gor! Ces - sa, cru -
f

19
f
rit.
a tempo
ppp
-del, tan - to ri - gor, tan - to ri - gor! Ca - ro mio
rit.
a tempo
f
ppp

22
mf
ben, cre - di - mi al - men, sen - za di te lan - gui - sce il
mf
25
p
cresc.
più cresc.
cor, ca - ro mio ben, cre - di - mi al - men, sen - za di
p
cresc.
più cresc.
28
f
p
rit.
te lan - gui - sce il cor.
rit.
colla voce
p
f
ff

[Blank page to facilitate page turns]

Group C

# Già la notte s'avvicina

*Already night is approaching, come oh Nice my dearest*
*To the calm seashore breathe in these fresh winds*
*You cannot know how delightful it is unless you stand on these sands*
*When a gentle breeze softly ripples the sea*

Words & music:
Isabella Colbran
1785-1845

In the exam do observe the repeats

(turn)

13
Non sa dir che sia di - let - to Chi non

15
po - sa in que - ste a - re - ne Or ch'un len - to zef - - fi -

18
-ret - to Dol - ce - men - te in cre - spa il mar.

21
Vie - ni o Ni - ce
Le fresch'

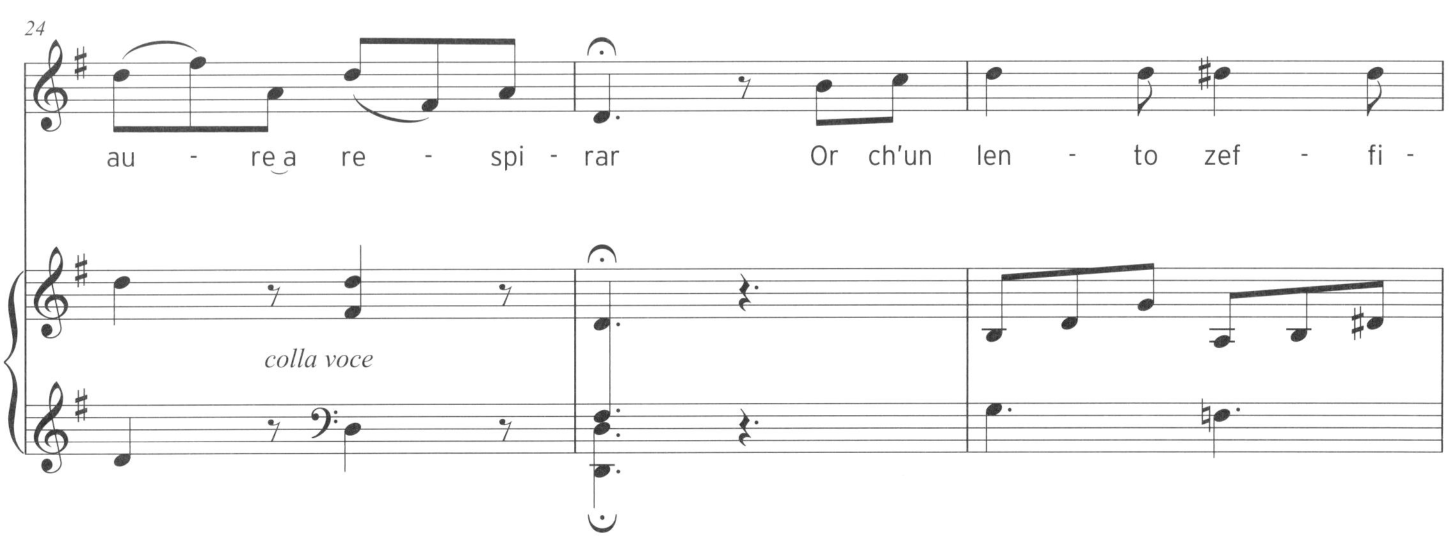
24
au - re a re - spi - rar
Or ch'un len - to zef - fi -
colla voce

27
-ret - to Dol - ce - men - te in cre - spa il mar